At Night

At Night

by Philip Ressner

photographs by Charles Pratt

E. P. Dutton & Co., Inc.   New York

The author and photographer are grateful to all those who helped in the making of the photographs in this book, including Patricia Broderick, Martin and Barbara Greene, Glynn and Cathy Hiller, Sid and Alice Mason, Frank and Aline McCann, James and Rochelle Patterson, Simon Ressner, Don and Penny Shankweiler, Elliot Willensky — and in particular Simpson Kalisher for his help in making the photograph on page 10.

For Lydia

At night, when most children are asleep, many things are different.

Smells and sounds are more important, and black is the main color. Darkness is all around, like the air. All little sounds are big, and in the quiet streets people talk more softly.

It is night over half the world.

In the house, the empty halls wait for the day.

The grown-ups talk and read,

watch television, look out at the stars, sleep.

In your room the only sound is of breathing.

Outside, the air smells secret.
The leaves in the trees rustle without being seen, and no birds sing.

The garden is only a dark smell in the dark.
Just beyond the fence around the field the world
ends.

Street lamps drop pale light all up and down the block; a grey cat turns orange in the light.

The garden is only a dark smell in the dark.
Just beyond the fence around the field the world
ends.

High up, the moon races through the clouds,

stopping when it reaches clear sky.

The roof across the street is darker than the sky.

Street lamps drop pale light all up and down the block; a grey cat turns orange in the light.

In the summer the ice cream truck comes by late, its silver bells silvery in the night.

The sidewalk surprises people's feet with ups and downs not there in the daylight.

The traffic light stands in the empty street, blinking red, green, red, green, all the night long.

The school gates are closed,

and in all the rooms there is no one;
at a window, only a paper fish looks out.

In the empty playground the wind tries out a swing or two just a little.

The candy store is locked, and a pearly light high in the ceiling makes big shadows.

Far off, a dog barks importantly at nothing important.

On the river, a boat whistle counts to three and stops.

Next door, a telephone rings and rings and rin—

It is night over half the world; soon it will be day.